The Great Songs of The Rolling Stones

GW00393393

Stones

Wise Publications
London/New York/Sydney/Paris/Copenhagen/Madrid

Exclusive distributors:
Music Sales Limited
8-9 Frith Street,
London W1V 5TZ,
England.
Music Sales Pty Limited
120 Rothschild Avenue
Rosebery, NSW 2018,
Australia.

Order No.AM959519
ISBN 0-7119-7460-8

Cover design by Studio Twenty.
Printed in Great Britain by
Printwise (Haverhill) Limited, Haverhill, Suffolk.

Your Guarantee of Quality
As publishers, we strive to produce every book to the highest commercial
standards. The book has been carefully designed to minimise awkward
page turns and to make playing from it a real pleasure. Particular care has
been given to specifying acid-free, neutral-sized paper made from pulps
which have not been elemental chlorine bleached. This pulp is from farmed
sustainable forests and was produced with special regard for the
environment. Throughout, the printing and binding have been planned to
ensure a sturdy, attractive publication which should give years of
enjoyment. If your copy fails to meet our high standards, please inform us
and we will gladly replace it.

Music Sales' complete catalogue describes thousands of titles and is
available in full colour sections by subject, direct from Music Sales Limited.
Please state your areas of interest and send a cheque/postal order for
£1.50 for postage to: Music Sales Limited, Newmarket Road, Bury St.
Edmunds, Suffolk IP33 3YB.

www.internetmusicshop.com

(This Could Be) The Last Time

Words & Music: Mick Jagger and Keith Richard

Moderate

5

last time, this could be the last time. May - be the

last time I don't know. Oh

no. Oh no. Well, I'm ———
Well, I ———
Well,

D. S. and Fade

Out Of Time

Words & Music: Mick Jagger and Keith Richard

7

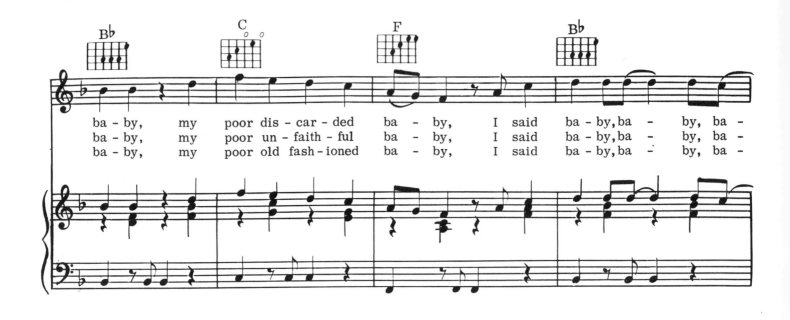

ba - by, my poor dis - car - ded ba - by, I said ba - by, ba - by, ba -
ba - by, my poor un - faith - ful ba - by, I said ba - by, ba - by, ba -
ba - by, my poor old fash - ioned ba - by, I said ba - by, ba - by, ba -

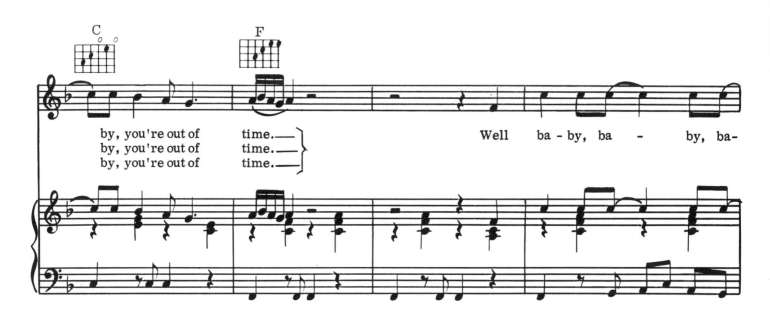

by, you're out of time.
by, you're out of time.
by, you're out of time.

Well ba - by, ba - by, ba -

by, you're out of time.

I said

ba - by, ba - by, ba - by, you're out of time. _____

Yes, you are left out; out of there with -

out a doubt, — 'cause ba - by, ba - by, ba - by, you're out of

1. 2. time.   3. time.

It's All Over Now

Words & Music: B. and S. Womack

pit-y how I cried; the ta-bles turn - ing now, her turn to cry.__

Be-cause I used to love her, but it's all o - ver now.

now. Be-cause I Well, I

used to wake the morn-ing, get my break-fast in bed.__ When I got ten

Lady Jane

Words & Music: Mick Jagger and Keith Richard

My sweet la - dy Jane, _____ when I see you a -
My dear la - dy Anne, _____ I've done what I
Oh, my sweet Mar - ie, _____ I wait at your

gain _____ your ser - vant am I; _____
can. _____ I must take my leave; _____
cue. _____ The sands have run out; _____

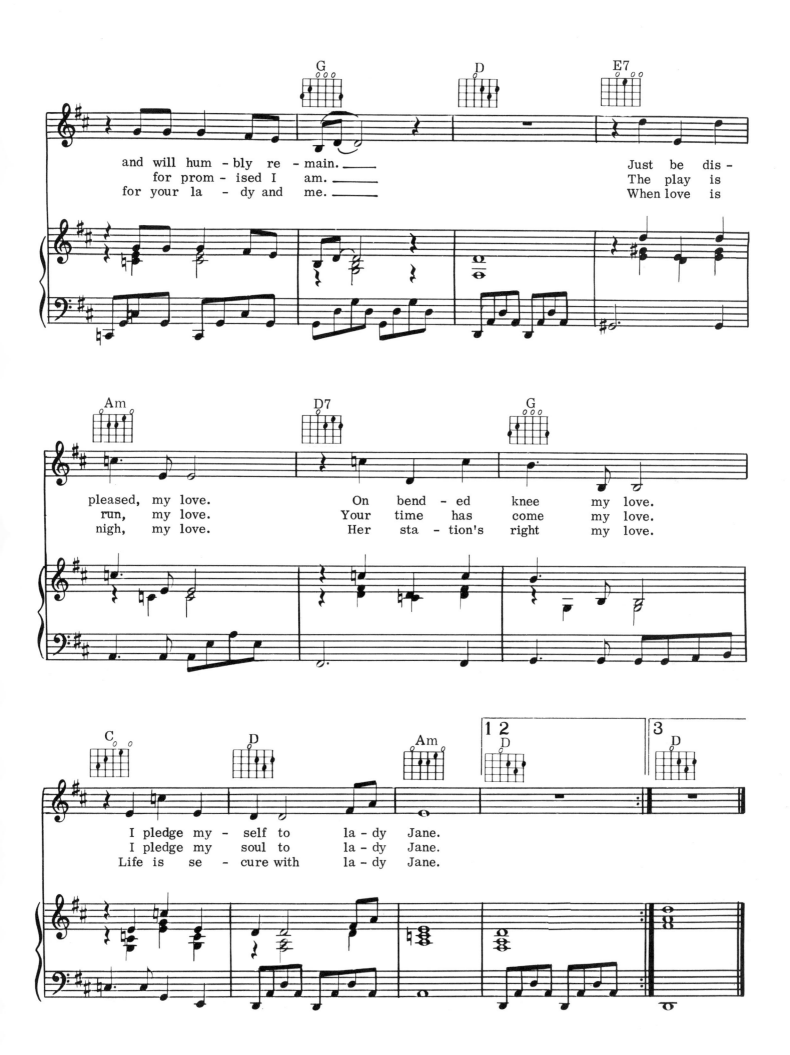

and will hum - bly re - main. _____
for prom - ised I am. _____
for your la - dy and me. _____

Just be dis -
The play is
When love is

pleased, my love.
run, my love.
nigh, my love.

On bend - ed knee my love.
Your time has come my love.
Her sta - tion's right my love.

I pledge my - self to la - dy Jane.
I pledge my soul to la - dy Jane.
Life is se - cure with la - dy Jane.

Have You Seen Your Mother, Baby

Words & Music: Mick Jagger and Keith Richard

I'm glad I o - pened your eyes. _____
I was just pass - ing the time. _____
Where have you been all your life? _____
You have take your choice at this time. _____

The have - nots would have tried _____ to
Talk-ing a - bout all the _____ peo - ple _____ who would

freeze you in ice. _____
try an - y - thing twice. _____

17

I'm all a - lone, won't you give_
The brave old world or the slide_

all your sym - pa - thy to
to the depths of de -

mine?_
cline._

Tell ___ me a sto - ry ___ a - bout how ___ you a - dore me, _ how we
Live ___ in the sha-dow, _ how we see ___ through the sha-dow, _ how we
Glimpse _ through the sha-dow, _ how we tear ___ at the sha-dow, _ how we
Hate ___ in the sha-dow, _ how we live ___ in your

sha - dow - y life. ___

CODA

Let It Bleed

Words & Music: Mick Jagger and Keith Richard

Well, we all ____ need some-one we can lean ____ on ____ And if you
need some-one we can bleed ____ on ____ And if you

want it, ____ Well, you can lean on me. ____ Yeah, we all ____
want to, ____ Well, you can bleed on me. ____ Yeah, we all ____

____ need some-one we can lean ____ on, ____ If you
____ need some-one we can bleed ____ on, ____ If you

23

Brown Sugar

Words & Music: Mick Jagger and Keith Richard

Gold ___ Coast slave ship bound for
Beat - ing, ___ cold Eng-lish
I bet your ma - ma was a

cot - ton fields, ___ sold ___ in a mar-ket down in New Or - leans. ___ Scarred
blood runs hot, ___ la ___ dy of the house won-d'rin where it's gon-na stop. House
Tent Show queen, ___ and ___ all her girl friends were sweet six - teen. ___ I'm

Midnight Rambler

Words & Music: Mick Jagger and Keith Richard

1. Did you hear a-bout the Mid-night Ram-bler?_ Ev-'ry-bod-y got to
2. (Did you hear a-bout the Mid-night Ram-bler?_ He'll leave his foot-prints up and down your

go. Did you hear a-bout the Mid-night Ram-bler,_ The
hall. Did you hear a-bout the Mid-night Ram-bler?_ Did you

one that shut the kitch-en door? He don't give a hoot of warn-
see me make my mid-night call? And if you catch the Mid-night Ram-

ing _____   wrapped up   in   a   black cat   cloak. _____   He
bler, _____   I'll   steal your mis-tress from un-der your nose.   Well, go

To Coda ⊕

don't go   in   the light   of   the morn - ing, _____   He's split, the time the cock-'rel
eas - y   with your cold   fan -   dan - go, _____   I'll   stick my   knife   right down your

crows.

Talk - in' 'bout the Mid - night   Ram-bler, _____   the   one you nev - er   seen   be - fore. _____

_____   Talk - in' 'bout the mid - night   gam - bler, _____   Did   you

29

Well, I'm talk - in' 'bout the mid - night gam - bler, ___ The

one you've nev - er seen be - fore. ___ Oh, don't do

that. Oh, don't do that. Oh, don't do that.

D.S. al Coda

Did you

Coda

(Spoken)

C9

throat! Ba - by, and it hurts!

Honky Tonk Women

Words & Music: Mick Jagger and Keith Richard

Blues rock

ff

Verse I

Ab   Db

I met a gin soaked, bar-room queen in Mem-phis, _____ She

Ab   Eb7

tried_ to take_ me up-stairs for a ride. _____ She

Ab   Db

had to heave me right_ a-cross her shoul-der _____ 'Cause I just_

Let's Spend The Night Together

Words & Music: Mick Jagger and Keith Richard

Jumpin' Jack Flash

Words & Music: Mick Jagger and Keith Richard

Bright Rock

1. I was born _____ in a cross-fire hur-ri-cane _____
2. (I was raised) _____ by a tooth-less, beard-ed hag, _____

And I howled _____ at my ma _____ in the driv-ing rain,
I was schooled _____ with a strap _____ right a-cross my back,

But it's all _____

You Can't Always Get What You Want

Words & Music: Mick Jagger and Keith Richard

Ruby Tuesday

Words & Music: Mick Jagger and Keith Richard

The Great Songs of George Harrison.

ISBN 0.7119.0562.2
Order No. AM37649

The Great Songs of Chris De Burgh.

ISBN 0.7119.0464.2
Order No. AM35536

The Great Songs of Michael Jackson.

ISBN 0.7119.0483.9
Order No. AM36401

The Great Songs of Stevie Wonder.

ISBN 0.7119.0421.9
Order No. AM34596

The Great Songs of The Police.

ISBN 0.7119.0550.9
Order No. AM37565

The Great Songs of Al Stewart.

ISBN 0.7119.0666.1
Order No. AM39587

The Great Songs of John Denver.

ISBN 0.7119.0563.0
Order No. AM37656

The Great Songs of The Carpenters.

ISBN 0.7119.0638.6
Order No. AM39108

The Great Songs of Barry Manilow.

ISBN 0.7119.0561.4
Order No. AM37631

The Great Songs of Cat Stevens.

ISBN 0.7119.0564.9
Order No. AM37664

The Great Songs of The Rolling Stones.

ISBN 0.7119.0593.2
Order No. AM38225

The Great Songs of Rod Stewart.

ISBN 0.7119.0680.7
Order No. AM39694

The Great Songs of Chicago.

ISBN 0.7119.0681.5
Order No. AM39702

The Great Songs of Gordon Lightfoot.

ISBN 0.7119.0391.3
Order No. AM34109

The Great Songs of Chris De Burgh.

ISBN 0.7119.0697.1
Order No. AM 39900

Great Songs, Great Series.

*The greatest songs by the greatest
performers and songwriters of our times.
A handsomely presented, very collectable set of beautifully engraved music,
all in full piano/vocal arrangements with complete lyrics,
guitar chord boxes and symbols.
The most economical way of buying sheet music today.*

*Available from your local music dealer,
or contact…
Music Sales Limited,
8/9 Frith Street,
London W1V 5TZ.*